D1402041

WHAT TO DO IF YOUR CHUTE

DOESN'T OPEN!

Survivors' Guide to the Last Days of the Coming Climate Inferno

JF CARPENTER
Illustrations by ALLIE DAIGLE

Visit: www.igiveachute.com

Cover and illustrations by Allie Daigle

ISBN: 979-8-88627-478-3

When stepping off in mid-air—hoping for a peaceful ride and gentle landing—one trusts that the person who packed their chute did it with care.
But when the chute doesn't open, trust is gone, the future looks quite dim even though extraordinarily picturesque at the moment.

Table of Contents

1

Overview

Well, it's 2022, and we have increased our carbon emissions and methane leaks worldwide, and we are losing the global warming battle as recorded by most of the folks watching the numbers. This is clear from the United Nations Intergovernmental Panel on Climate Change (IPCC) report, August 2021, which signaled an alarm (code red) because of the lack of progress toward reducing global warming since the Paris Agreement, 2015. Also in late 2021, the United Nations Climate Change Conference (COP26) met for the twenty-sixth time but failed to record significant progress toward reducing CO2eq[1] in the atmosphere from the hugest emitting countries.

UN Secretary-General António Guterres opened COP26 with an urgent warning: "We are digging our own graves … recent climate action announcements might give the impression that we are on track to turn things around. This is an illusion. Even in the best-case scenario, temperatures will rise well above 2 degrees Celsius (3.6 degrees Fahrenheit) and likely quite a bit higher. We are still heading for climate disaster." [2]

It is not to say that there is not a broad group of sincere organizations and citizens of the world that have been/are working hard to curb the chemicals that threaten our existence. They

---

[1] The *eq* after C02 signifies *carbon dioxide equivalent*. This is a metric measure used to compare the emissions from various greenhouse gases based on their global warming potential (GWP). Other greenhouse gases are methane, nitrous oxide, and ozone.

[2] António Guterres, UN Secretary General, opening remarks COP26 (UN Climate Summit) Glasgow, Scotland, November 1, 2021.

are out there, but the job seems to be beyond the good people's ability to guide the planet into a space that will allow humans to occupy earth for much longer. I know, we are not supposed to talk like that. The sanctioned position has always been blind optimism bolstered by a grin and the call to dig deeper, but today—or maybe it was sometime yesterday—the grin became **grim**, and the diggers have become **reapers.**

The simple facts have led us to a realization that must not be mentioned; no, it's not Lord Voldemort but some equally inconvenient truth.

We are not losing the global warming battle—**the battle is lost!**

Admittedly, this is an unpopular realization, but the forces that have been and are presently in power have little interest in taking the necessary steps to reign in the established economic barons that rule the air of the world. As a result, we will have a host environment that will not at first be friendly and later will no longer be habitable by present-day homo sapiens.

Oh, I get it; if you believed me or science or the scientists that have been warning of this day for decades, you'd be asking, "What can we do?" "We are (used to be) the most powerful nation in the world, and we will put a stop to this!" But it doesn't matter because the time has come, we are past the tipping point and there isn't anything anybody can do to save the planet. Think massive meteor hurling directly at the earth from a galaxy far, far away. It is over for humans. From this point forward, isolated geographic suffering will morph into coastal malaise, grassland dysfunction, and highland congestion before terminal destruction.

So given all this doom and gloom stuff, the real question is, what can/should I do now with the indeterminate time I/we have while I/we have it? And so, we have come to the actual value of this soliloquy. Should we run, give up, fight, or get smart about our remaining options for the time we have left? What do you want to do or see before it's all gone? What should your kids see today that won't be here tomorrow? What investments are ripe for the destruction era? Where should I relocate before the masses figure this out? Can I start eating meat, take up smoking, buy a nuclear car?

The global cooling chute did not open for planet Earth, and little now can be done about that. Still, there may be twenty or thirty years of climatic withering that you can enjoy before planetary dissonance makes life miserable.

4

Let's get started.

The sooner the realization that we have lost the campaign to curb global temperature settles in, the better you will prepare for the coming couple of decades. Most things are not going to happen all at once, although more than half the world's species are already on the move northward (butterflies, moose, humans). Others will migrate because their warming environment will no longer support life as they knew it (Atlantic mackerel, caribou, humans). The point is that you have some planning time and it should not be wasted because the world is already changing due to increased temperatures (fires, floods, and storms).

While not as predictable as a tidal wave, this coming surge of global heating will most likely start with the waters. They are rising, acidifying, flooding, degrading, and disappearing. So if you are committed to being on the planet longer than others, you have to have a plan. It's going to get hotter for longer, and in some places, a lot hotter. It will be dirtier, more violent, less healthy, and more brutal. This is not fiction or a scare tactic; I have no dog in this hunt.

For too long, we have depended on the undependable to guide us in times of trouble and strife; we've probably made some mistakes there. We hoped for fifty years that our leaders would have the peoples of the world in their prayers and make good long-term decisions that would preserve an increasingly productive and sustainable future for all creatures of the planet. They lost their way somewhere on that continuum.

So now, it's up to you to make the most of the remaining temperate time you have here. I hope that the coming pages will help you create your vision for future action—or at least help you think more reflectively about what/who comes first. The sooner you start, the better you'll be able to make your and your children's children's future more comfortable. It is discon certing to think about preparing children for an environmental-ly hostile world. Still, much like getting one's affairs in order before death, it has become an obligation of the living.

Carbon-Carbon-Carbon

We've got some brilliant people working on carbon reduction and some that are not so smart. Others, like oil and gas companies disguised as concerned corporate citizens, have pitched in with money and ideas designed to keep the "pure of spirit" busy while buying a few more years of pollution production. One has to be on guard when solutions for global cooling come from those that stand the least to gain by an environmental renaissance. I guess this deception is a good idea if you're an oil company executive nearing retirement age without grandchildren, but for everybody else, not so good.

There are not many people who have not heard that we have a "hot air" problem. They used to call it air pollution, but that had a negative connotation; today, it's just a carbon problem. Cool, the oil and gas companies got rid of millions of centrists who think the air has or will significantly improve by air scrubbing. Next, we'll see Willy Wonka building big machines to scrub the air before we breathe it. These efforts are not going to work or certainly will not work in time for the planet to reach temperature control goals to make the earth livable in 2050. Not that it matters at this point: no amount of scrubbing, scraping, or drawing down of airborne CO_2 will reverse the planet's warming. That is if we ever really wanted to cool it down. We've had a verbal full-court press on the anti-coolers for over a decade, and all that has happened is that the planet has gotten warmer and we've burned more coal, drilled more leaky gas wells, and taken more clean energy sources off line—not cool! Let's face it, a warmer planet, even one that will kill us all, is just not today's problem. When it gets dire, we'll solve it. In the meantime, buy an F-250 truck, disperse the leaves with your gas-powered leaf blower, hook up the boat and its two-stroke engine, and head out to what's left of the lake to catch some of those mercury-fortified fish you're not supposed to eat.

It breaks my heart; I love this planet—this country. I am not ready to let it go. The time we've had together has been good—perfect—but too brief. "Alas, poor mother earth, I knew her well."[3] But it is time to be realistic, face the music, and prepare to meet the lack of future with a humble sigh and a fuck you to all the people who could have and didn't band together to save this planet for the things that live here.

---

[3] This is a bastardization of a Shakespearian quote from "Hamlet." The truth is, it's based on one of the most famous lines in theatre, which Hamlet never actually said: "Alas poor Yorick, I knew him well." The correct reading is, "Alas, poor Yorick. I knew him, Horatio." William Shakespeare, "Hamlet," in *My Shakespeare*, (myshakespear.com), line 169.

Relocation

Not everyone will be able to take advantage of a preemptive environmental relocation, but you will. Recently, it was reported that the best locations to delay the adverse effects of global warming would be around the Great Lakes states. These areas are away from the impact of rising sea levels, not top of mind for hot relocation destinations. They are cool now but will become Mediterranean as the globe starts to cook. Some municipalities in these areas are already advertising and attracting new residents from the fire-torn regions of Northern California and the soggy environs of the Gulf Coast.[4] I'm not kidding; this is already happening, so start to get mentally and, if you can, physically in motion.

Others will be relocating as well, so late starters will face competition. Look what happened in Idaho when Californians and Oregonians decided to flee San Francisco, Silicon Valley, and even Portland in 2020–2021. Boise went from a sleepy value-laden college town in the middle of nowhere to the place that ranked number one in housing price escalation in early 2022.

Folks will continue to move out of the areas of unavoidable inevitabilities to more stable inland environs where the weather will be less hostile, prices more moderate, and the chance of a prolonged survival possible. But this will cause problems. We have already seen how mass migration from Africa and Central America has pushed the world's fragile political stability to the brink as leaders struggle with polarized constituencies to find a humane perspective for national and international exodus in an already changed world. If at all possible, make your generational relocation decisions early.

One more complication to consider for those of you fortunate enough to have the choice to rearrange your whereabouts in these twilight years. Country escapes are tempting but complicated. Yes, you'll be dry, maybe even cooler, but you will be cut off. Unless you opt for the survivalist lifestyle, supply chain issues will be a factor for country folks. People, cities, and regions will still need goods and services, even in a disorientated world. Clusters of economic clout usually associated with significant economic areas will unavoidably receive more goodies than isolated areas, which will become difficult and dangerous to provision. By this point, it may not matter at all, but it may. As you triangulate your resting spot, consider the full array of benefits and maybe leave the isolated, palatial cabin at the lake to someone less analytical.

This points us to an unanticipated respite—yes, the city. For those who can't flee, some towns will decay and become even more complicated and alarming than they already have. But those located away from lowland saltwater intrusion and on major supply routes will have amenities to offer. You'll still have to fight for food, but it will get there, as will medical teams and supplies. Housing will dip, and if your timing is right, it might even be a bargain. Many of the other site selection criteria we have reviewed need to come into play as you conjure your solution, but there will be an alternative to the county life.

You are planning for an unimaginable future, so take a comprehensive view of what areas will be the most tolerable climatically and the safest socially and politically, and choose your

---

[4] Kate Yoder, "Fleeing Global Warming? 'Climate Havens' Aren't Ready Yet," Wired, December 11, 2021, Science, https://www.wired.com/story/fleeing-global-warming-climate-havens-arent-ready-yet/.

neighbors wisely; they will be even more important than they are today.

Neighbors

You've been spending more time at home, and this will continue when not engaged in relocation excursions. The people on either side of you and across the street need to be there to look after your place and your stuff until you can relocate to somewhere that will provide safe residential longevity for you and your heirs. If you can-not secure stable, cooperative agreements, your neighbors may become your most significant threat. They see your stuff; they know what you have and how weak your defenses are. Differences in ideology, politics, religion, race, and scarcity will stress the bonds used to hold neighborhoods together. The increase in tension caused by the erratic availability of heating oil in the frigid winter, intermittent air conditioning during the sweltering summer, delays, and cancellations of everyday assuries to which we've become accustomed in the past will reveal deep-seated personal differences. The pandemic of 2020–2022 has shown us that stress on humans increases their basic tendencies to distrust people who are different and to lash out at targets of convenience at the slightest provocation. This pattern will get intense.

Tomorrow's neighborhoods will take on different roles in our societies. They will not be homogenous from one place to another. Relocating will depend more and more on finding the right community rather than the right house as the world ghettoizes for the coming climatic and social disintegration. Even the well-planned relocation may not be a long-term solution for your security problems but one, if chosen well, that will prolong a sense of wellbeing until the moat
is constructed and the drawbridge raised.

Protein Eating

You are what you eat, as they say, and if you are presently an enjoyer of the non-vegetarian fare, this is your era. We consume more animal-based food than anywhere in the world. We grew up on it, and we love it to death. It doesn't matter that the animal industry is one of the largest suppliers of pollutants, driving up global temperatures. Between bovine belching and farting, pastureland degradation, ruinous soil disruptions, insecticides, and plain old getting to market, carbon emissions are killing "The Goose That Laid the Golden Eggs."[5] "While chasing after hopes of a treasure, I lost the profit I held in my hands."[6] If it mattered in a post save-the-planet world, I'd be telling you to stop eating meat and encouraging you to try to get used to one of the newly developed nearly meat plant substitutes. But we are past that point now, so burger away knowing that the availability of this fine fare will start to diminish as a struggling world reevaluates what's important for a threatened species.

---

[5] Aesop, "The Goose That Laid the Golden Eggs," in Aesop's Fables, ed. and trans. Laura Gibbs (Oxford: Oxford University Press, 2002), p. 434.

[6] Aesop, "The Goose That Laid the Golden Eggs," p. 434.

I have not acquired a taste for worms, grasshoppers, and banana slugs, but if I were going to be here for a while longer than 2040, I definitely would. These are high protein foods, which will be necessary for the survivors and the last of our species who will inherit our past environmental indiscretions. I'm sure you already know that in beef cattle circles, bovines consider themselves endangered. Hell, if a steer lives to be three years old, he is the herd elder. They are on the way out because, while they are not on the endangered species list, they will not survive the realization that they are a prime emitter of CO_2.

Oh, rich people will have them to the end, but you and I will need to develop a taste for the more exotic—you know, things that live under, in, and below where we are used to getting our food.

Soon, someone will figure out that cattle production is killing us and the planet. Cholesterol, obesity, bacon, and carbon are the premium products of our meat-eating obsession. Many have already died from the first three, and the last will get the rest of us in a short time. But worrying about this is in the past; we are moving forward with the food we should be eating that may not be available in the next several generations. Most of us have already given up spotted owl, polar bear, and manatee, so we can push along and focus on the protein sources most likely to be the target of a populous that has realized that protein production is hastening our demise. You guessed it, cattle are the number one agricultural source of greenhouse gasses worldwide."[7] If we are going to survive, they will need to go soon. But for now, what the heck, enjoy...

---

[7] Amy Quinton, "Cows and Climate Change," ucdasvis.edu, June 27, 2019, https://www.ucdavis.edu/food/news/making-cattle-more-sustainable.

Best Hamburger Ever

- 1½ lb. ground beef, lean
- ½ onion, chopped
- ½ cup cheddar cheese, shredded
- 1 egg
- 1 oz. onion soup, dry
- 1 tsp. soy sauce
- 1 tsp. Worcestershire sauce
- 1 clove garlic
- 1 tbsp. garlic powder
- 1 tsp. parsley, dried
- 1 tsp. basil, dried
- 1 tsp. oregano, dried
- ½ tsp. rosemary, dried, crushed
- Salt & pepper to taste[8]

Reflecting on this position, it might be better to get used to eating burgers and ribs outside of the house. This way, you can begin to train the generations that will not have meat in the future that "near meat" is quite tasty. I know teaching your kids to eat bugs isn't going to be easy, but it will be a survival skill they will need in the new world. It's hard to say how much time you have, and I guess it depends on your age when reading this, but if your job is to prepare your future progeny for the horrors of a global bust, meat-eating will not be on the menu.

---

[8] Univstudent, "Best Hamburger Ever," allrecipies, 2022, https://www.allrecipes.com/recipe/72657/best-hamburger-ever.

Personal Healthcare

We pretty much take this for granted at whatever level we currently experience it, whether it be socialized, universal, pay as you go, or barely available. Healthcare will get a lot worse as we slip down the unpredictable slope of social disorder egged on by global warming and the unexpected complications that will come in its wake.

Today, the pandemic challenges our systems in ways we did not anticipate—for example, the need for new vaccines, the burnout of healthcare workers, the dissensus among medical professionals, and the manipulation of the world's peoples through partisan health advice by disingenuous politicians.

It will be more important than ever to keep you and your loved ones as healthy as possible as we approach our warming planet's future. The strong and healthy will survive the longest and be the most comfortable. As we saw during the recent viral assault of COVID-19, the vulnerable and least protected died first. If we ever had an incentive to get/stay in shape, it should be the fear of an early, painful demise. The healthcare system, plagued by limited resources and overuse due to scarcity of medical professionals, supplies, and disfigured supply chains, will not exist as it does today. Life on this future hot sphere will be mercilessly uncomfortable for some and, for others, a death sentence.

Employment

If you are fortunate enough to have a transportable job in an industry with a high survivability quotient, then you can live anywhere you want as long as the communication networks remain reliable and you're willing to take pay cuts. But what if you are a regular Jane and are looking to develop climate change-resistant skills? What directions should you and your kids be exploring? For you, technology is probably your greatest friend and enemy. What skills and services will be least threatened by climatic disruptions and what is your backup source of income if "Plan A" doesn't work? Services will be in demand, especially in medical and technical areas—did I mention air conditioning repair? Remember, making money today is important, as we will discuss, so you have to increase your earnings while you can. Certainly, you want to stay away from pool and landscape maintenance, government work (dwindling tax revenue), banking, or anything that uses a combustion engine and everything that can be done better through automation and big data.

Now, on the proactive side of future employment, there will be many new occupations developing: crypt relocation, seawall and levy restorer, nematode and cricket ranching, aboveground sanitation engineer, ammunition reloader, shade products sales, and below-grade home construction. The good news is that there will be plenty of work; the bad news is there won't be anything to eat.

It's the Little Things

Recycling: One of the good things about hurtling toward a "Pop-Tart" planet is that all the little things we used to feel compelled to do to save our humble home are no longer necessary. Recycling, for instance, doesn't make any sense. I mean, many folks already know that most of the stuff we pushed into those reuse barrels wasn't being recycled anyway. We stopped trying to make recycling work a while ago. China didn't want our discards anymore, and those countries that take them are overwhelmed with the stuff the rest of the world sends. If we ever stop paying them to take it, it's over. I mean, it is over now; it's just another reality we don't want to face in this environmentally hostile world. The point here is to stop feeling guilty about not recycling; it is just too late to make a difference, even if we had taken the time to wash out all the mayonnaise containers and separate the metal lids from the jars that we tossed into those bins. You are free, and you just picked up some valuable under-counter real estate.

Plastic Bottles: We don't have to worry about disposable plastic bottles either. These were one of the world's great conveniences. For Westerners, the need to stay hydrated was only a dollar away. You didn't have to drink from a contaminated municipal fountain, and you could just drop the empty bottle in the recycling bin or the trash; it all went to the same place.

Plastic bottles did mean clean drinking water for third-world inhabitants where that commodity was often in short supply. The plastic crackdown made it even more difficult for those people to access safe water for baby formula, medical treatments, and general community health. While there is still clean water to drink, the return to plastic bottles will save lives in third-world countries. On the other hand, plastic in the sea will be a growing problem right up until our end, and then that problem will solve itself.

Plastic Bags: Plastic bags are a different problem; they are plain ugly. Freeway fences are littered with bags of different sizes and shapes in an unattractive pattern that would embarrass any Cristo understudy. We should have done away with these annoyances years ago, but we didn't want to. And now, we have shared them with the rest of the world, and we will have them in one form or another forever. I read one report that said microplastics in the great garbage patches were good because they reflected sunlight and contributed to global cooling; I wonder what oil company employed that writer? Anyway, the weighty consumer conundrum, "plastic or paper," will live on until there is so little of both that we'll be forced to carry our multi-use satchels and use them until they fall apart, and then we'll be forced to recycle them.

Showers: I've come to take short showers because I live in an area where water is scarce for much of the year. If one is environmentally concerned, this conservation could be done every day to help save water or only a couple of times a week if one lives alone. The point is, if we've lost the battle to save the planet, I guess short showers are not as important as they once were; it's like saving money to leave to kids who hate you. Business and political leaders worldwide may have set up this crisis, but they have shown little interest in fixing it. So now, why should we be inconvenienced by something we are powerless to improve?

Coffee: I love coffee, but even if I didn't, I'd be concerned about its future and my pleasure. A warming world does not support the cultivation of this legalized drug we so fancy. Over 50 percent of the coffee terroir is threatened by the present rate of change in temperatures. Heat acceleration will degrade the taste of our brew of choice and further increase the price and reduce availability. I'm not sure I can drink more coffee than I already do, but from now on, each sip will be greeted with the reverence of a kiss goodbye.

It is interesting to note that coffee has never been an environmental friend. It is second only to water as the humanoid drink of choice, and a drop in demand won't be all bad, as coffee cultivation is one of the leading causes of deforestation of rainforests around the globe[9] —if only we had stopped drinking coffee sooner.

---

[9] J. Lee, "How Coffee Aids in Deforestation of Our Rainforests," Going Green Today, 2014, http://blog.goinggreentoday.com/how-coffee-aids-in-deforestation-of-our-rainforests/.

Adventures with Loved Ones

This is really what it is all about. Since we can no longer save the world, let's make the most of what we have while we have it. Grab your kids, loved ones, or even some people you don't know and get out and enjoy this beautiful ecosphere.

As you put together a blueprint for the coming generation or two, a simple prioritization should help give new meaning to family planning. You'll want to know which natural resources are likely to go first, second, and so on, and you should estimate when the rest of the general population is expected to figure out that this stuff is not going to be there anymore.

Forests and areas with large trees will be the most protected in the pre-apocalyptic era. These old-growth giants are working overtime to filter and capture the increase in atmospheric carbon. And while younger trees scoop up far less carbon than their older kind, they will still provide unique places to relax and ponder the beauty of a dying species. Although, you might want to leave these forests until the last—because they will be heavily guarded by state militias who will protect their filtering functions—there is a caveat. Militia guns won't stop a fire. We almost lost some of the oldest redwoods on the planet during the summer of 2021 due to drought-induced wildfires in California. If you haven't seen these gigantic marvels, maybe you can stop by and check them out on your next relocation excursion before next summer's or next year's wildfires put an end to their reign.

You won't be the first to travel to Africa to caravan through the savanna searching for wild animals, and you don't want to be the last. This will be an experience you and everyone with you-will remember like it was yesterday for the rest of their lives.

This again needs to be on the "do it now" list because there is less of it to see every day that passes. Being with "lions and tigers and bears, oh my,"[10] is a real treat, to say nothing of the elephants, giraffes, and zebras. This viewing has been under siege for many years, and it's just one environmental or political click from destruction. It is hard to say who will destroy these residents of the Serengeti first; the poachers, the governments, the tourists, or the environment, but everybody is after them. Buildings and natural wonders will be on the planet a lot longer than these majestic creatures will be able to endure; shame on us! Don't overthink this; just do it.

I don't have to tell you that water is big, everybody's favorite. So this might be an excellent place to start building a plan in the short term. Pristine water still exists, Lake Tahoe in California, some Florida Keys, Kiritimati in the Pacific, and Seychelles in the western Indian Ocean. These and other water bodies will provide the thrill and freedom of discovery and untouched

---

[10] Harold Arlen, "Lions and Tigers and Bears, Oh My," The Wizard of Oz, directed by Victor Fleming (Culver City, CA: Metro-Goldwyn-Mayer, 1939).

wonder, but don't linger. In the recent past, we lost the beaches and some of the cenotes in Tulum, Mexico, and parts of the Great Barrier Reef on the east coast of Australia. Seek the remaining unique places out and go, but don't tell everyone. We will not have these long due to the warming waters, increased pollution from underdeveloped sanitation, downriver affluents, and just too many people. Get there first and keep your mouth shut about it; it is probably good advice to keep your mouth shut in all of these waters. Remember, the battle is lost, and no second chance is available to our offspring. It is now or never. Be a person of action before we become the action for some other organisms, and you, who are on the road, "teach your children well."[11]

Oh, if you're the type of person who likes to go where few have gone, make advanced reservations for the "over the top" cruise that will leave from Valdez, Alaska, and transverse the Northwest Passage through the melted polar ice fields. Due to post-industrialized planetary warming, the polar ice cap has continually melted. In 2007, the passage opened up to commercial vessels, and with the continued increase in temperatures, it is expected that tourist travel will commence shortly. If you are patient and lucky enough to be around toward mid-century, the ice cap will be so compromised that it is estimated that sea travel will be directly over the top of the pole. While not terrific for most polar living things, this catastrophe could provide a unique experience for you; you may as well take advantage of it. You'll be among the first to see and be seen by creatures that, well, haven't ever experienced anything like you and may never again.

---

[11] Crosby, Stills, Nash & Young, vocalists, "Teach Your Children," by Graham Nash, Déjà Vu, Atlantic, 1970, Album.

23

Glaciers

If I were looking for something else to put near the top of the "do it now" list, it would be visiting glaciers. These are present all over the world—but not for long. They are melting at alarming rates, even in Montana. We are holding a contest to rename the national park there because Glacier just doesn't cut it anymore. If you were to go there thinking about getting up close and personal with a glacier, you'd better be able to hike up to the residual or save your money for the helicopter ride. The same is true for parts of Alaska. I hiked for a half-hour past signs that said "The glacier used to be here" before reaching the foot of what is now not such an impressive ice flow.

Nobody likes bad news, and solid evidence of extreme global warming when one just wants to have a good time on vacation can be a bummer. "Facts are stubborn things,"[12] quipped John Adams. Almost everywhere we turn in the world these days, we have glaciers melting at rates we have not recorded in recent times. So please, make this a priority because they are going for good. Oh, and don't forget to enter the renaming contest (see appendix); BTW, "Hot Springs National Park" has already been submitted.

---

[12] John Adams, Portable John Adams (City of Westminster: Penguin Books, 2004).

24

Travel Cautions

You want to be ahead of the many others who will come to realize that the time for planning has passed and the time for action has probably passed as well. But journeys begin when the boat is loaded and not before. So take advantage of your ability to travel. That excursion experience will be normal in the short run, but this will not be the case for as long as you would like. We have already seen many of our reflection sites (Florida beaches, U.S. Capital) become corrupted. A run through an Atlanta suburb can be lethal; a trip to the desert, fatal, or a peaceful walk to the corner store, life-threatening. Unfortunately, this pattern will become more acute. As travelers in this and especially the next decade, you will need to be on guard at all times.

The unevenly distributed awareness that the end is within sight has and will continue to give license to those with less to lose. The psychological construct that strips hope from our being is the catalyst for social disorganization. Traveler's today are warned not to give one-finger salutes to other motorists in Southern California for fear of being shot. Others council— don't stand out, don't look like a tourist. Remember that being in some places makes you appear to be a person of means and therefore a target in this coming epoch of scarcity.

Respites for travelers, like Walmart parking areas and rest stops on freeways, are still places to take a break. But they will be more than that in the future. They will become target-gathering points for the hopeless to exercise their disappointment about how hot or cold or wet it has become and how helpless they are to do anything about it. Unfortunately, for those of you who are late to relocate, the road will not be friendly, and "there will be no code that we will all live by."[13] Ciphers of global warming today will be symbols of global panic in the future. Gas and diesel vehicles, green lawns, swimming pools, and extra pets will all attract the angst of local vigilantes whose actions against climate destroyers will highlight the pain of the everyman of the day.

Are we there right now? Well, no. But we are closer than we would like to believe. Don't wait to get out there and do some of the things we have discussed because, seriously, one day soon, that RV in the driveway is going to be a more significant liability than you ever imagined. You're not even going to have to leave home to get the travel danger experience.

---

[13] Crosby, Stills, Nash & Young, "Teach Your Children."

27

Electric Transportation

Even though the future will not be what we'd hoped it would be, there is still plenty of time to buy one of the lit electric cars coming onto the market. Tesla EVs are ubiquitous where I live, but there is serious competition on the way. Soon, we will see Lucid Air Pure, Ford F-150 Lightning, Hyundai Lonig 5, Frisker Ocean, Rivian R1S, and ten other fresh models from manufacturers old and new. This is going to be an excellent place to spend money. Each unit contributes to slowing the death of the planet, and if we can slow it down in any way, we should all be doing our part. There is no reason why we can't have some fun during these declining days.

Space Travel

Now here is a bright spot. It is no wonder that Elon Musk and Jeff Bezos and a group of other brilliant people are spending a ton of today's dollars on rocket-based panic rooms. What do they know that they are not telling us? Even NASA is getting on the bandwagon! You may have seen Moon or Red Mars. The word is out, and the smart guys aren't waiting for everybody else to get on board; they are just doing it. This is a massive undertaking that the rich boys will not entrust to their governments. Even people like Captain Kirk, who respectfully will not live long enough to be on the first escape pod, had to get up there and look around before he got beamed up or down— probably not meaningful which way.

How can you participate in the space escape? Make a boatload of money and sign your kids up. Sorry, this is how it is going to work. How many people do we need to save our species? No one knows, but we'll send as many as we can to as many possibilities as we can before it happens, and it will be a lot more than two of each sex. So to review, you'll need to be rich, young, strong, healthy, and a potential procreator. I'm sure the ads for Pilgrims read somewhat differently, and the impetus was not the same. We're talking about the saving of our asses—I mean species.

There is a form at the end of this book for early registration to be considered for space colonization. All information about your selected candidate or child will be confidential so the Dementors or the Russians won't be able to capture your intent and identity. Your registration requests for Fly Me to the Moon will be forwarded to Elon Musk—Space X—and Jeff Bezos—Blue Origin.

Investing in the Apocalypse

We may as well make some money while we are enjoying our last few "normal" years with our loved ones. This realization that we are just not going to make it provides an advantage to those looking for opportunities. They will be everywhere in the near term as the "denying body" moves forward in a business as usual posture. Let's briefly look at some of the big winners.

Nuclear Everything: Nuclear power is now as green as green can be, and we know longer have to worry about the number one concern, nuclear waste. As Daddy Warbucks said, "You don't have to be nice to the people you meet on the way up if you're not coming back down again."[14]

France, Japan, and the United States have all started to reverse their stance on this utility, and the money has begun to flow; get here early. Nuclear energy solutions and investments have already started to blossom. Bill Gates is building small modular reactors [SMR] for the home and small businesses; they're being used for space travel and water desalinization. Once more, as people realize that we are not going to come anywhere near saving the planet as we know it, all objections (cost, waste disposal, terrorism) will disappear. The quiet atomic revolution will surface as a megatrend.

Moving Industries: We already saw in 2021 substantial shifts away from cities and high congestion points to more pastoral environs. This trend will continue as the mobile populous tries to outrun the climatic and social turmoil of our now substan

---

[14] Annie, directed by Bob Marshall (Los Angeles, CA: Columbia Tri Star Television, 1999).

tially warming planet. This play on relocation companies will not be for the long haul, but I believe this will be a notable trend for the moribund investing crowd. This is a get-in soon suggestion, but stay on guard for a rapid exit as relocation problems overwhelm the financial and practical advantages.

Clothing: We are in for a sea change here—but not the type you might be expecting. The garment and shoe industries contribute 8 percent to the world's total greenhouse gas development.[15] In our quest to stay up with the "Jones," retailers and internet enablers pushed cheap fashion for everyone until we reached a new level in our disposable world. It has had a devastating impact on our landfills, carbon production, and artisans worldwide that have not been able to compete with all the new throw-away clothing. I guess we reap what we sew.

The pressure on this segment will be substantial in the decline of the winter coat era. But there will be opportunities: durable, lightweight fabrics (bamboo and hemp); earth responsible companies, such as 10 Tree and Patagonia; recyclers, such as ThredUp; and small closet construction ventures, like ThinBox, are already here. And many more will be on their way as the last-ditch effort to cool the planet fails.

War Industries: As we'll discuss later, it is a low probability that global warming, plastic congestion, or rising sea levels will put an end to us all, but those events will contribute to the social and geopolitical turmoil that will be faced by our children and our children's children. For now, let's stick to our investment topic and simply say, war machine products and services will see unimaginable demand as climate change realities

---

[15] Paul Hawken, ed., *Regeneration Ending the Climate Crisis in One Generation* (New York: Penguin Random House, 2021).

escalate the scarcity quotient and the people of this world scramble to protect themselves and get what's left. The goods and materials of survival will demand a premium whether you're an investor, a prepper, or someone who just wants to see how the fourth quarter plays out. The preceding nuclear category fits nicely here, but so do so many others: concrete, armaments, water purification, and underground construction, to mention a few.

Technology: Many of our technological advancements have been funded through the federal government, both for offensive and defensive military purposes. This trend will continue going forward as the civil, cultural, and international unrest ramps-up and climatic pressures become the catalyst for increasingly desperate peoples to take action. Watch what the government is funding and look for its private sector adaptations. Water and air purification, small modular reactors (SMR), advanced machine learning (AI and big data), fashion-oriented bulletproof vests, chemicals for rainmaking, and yes, maybe even cold fusion is on the buy list.

Seaweed: We will eat more of it, use it for fuel, and feed cattle to reduce carbon emissions. But we'll have to learn how to keep the oceanic pH factors in control, so we don't kill it all off—as we are in California—before we discover its life-saving and enhancing qualities. The investment cycle is just beginning here, and we should see a big run-up as companies learn to capitalize on seaweed's unique properties.

Healthcare: This industry will grow with or without the problems caused by increasing temperatures. Much like how the world's decision-makers underestimated COVID-19, so will the healthcare demand augmented by climatic catastrophe be misdiagnosed. Heck, we could barely keep up with the novelty of the new virus in 2021. Can you imagine how increased heat, nonedible insect migration, overflowing sewage plants, rat infestation, and viral warfare will drive the need to keep the old and infirm safe, the young alive, and the middle-aged viable and procreating long enough to care for everybody else? We will become a populace of pragmatic healthcare providers— think "Soylent Green." But before we get there, we will spend mountains of plastic money avoiding the inevitable, *Don't Look Up*.[16] You can be in on the ground floor by simply investing in inland-based companies that have led the way in healthcare innovations in the past. This is not rocket science; there won't be much time for innovation and research. The companies currently performing will be the only ones with the financial and intellectual staying power to be there when resources are stretched to the limit. Invest in medical blue chips.

Real Estate: We can't overlook this segment. I've been talking about it for pages now without directly linking the investment

---

[16] Don't Look Up, directed by Adam McKay (Boston, MA: Hyperobject Industries, 2021).

value of this asset class to unfriendly geographic locations, migration shifts, and climate risk calculations. Not all property will increase in the future. Still, if one can triangulate climate security, affordability, clean water, local electrical power, and supply chain surety, you'll have the core of the equation. Other variables—like political stability and social compatibility—will be necessary as a resident but maybe not so much as an investor. It seems like every week a national magazine publishes a list of the best small towns in which to relocate. Some are even offering cash incentives to relocate to those with specific skills or internet-based jobs. Others are making their moves now; there are opportunities out there.

Oh, and if you are a gambler or a disbeliever, you might consider investments in waterfront properties, marinas, or reuse options for wind and solar farms—just sayin'.

Electricity: I mentioned earlier that opportunities will be everywhere during this transition period. The world will be transitioning from fossil fuels to electricity however they decide to source it (earth, wind, or fire). Power companies are heavily regulated and an unlikely investment powerhouse, but everything around electricity should be ecstatic. Parts, pieces, metals, transmission, alternative generation, stoves, cars, heaters, buses, coolers, trains, planes, tankers—well, you get the idea. You might be too early for some, already too late for others, but there is something here for everyone.

Capital: One final word here—well, maybe more than a word. The roasting world of tomorrow will have something in common with the heating world of today—wealth. No matter what you are doing to support yourself at this time, it will be more important going forward. Money well spent today may make tomorrow possible. We will all try to navigate these decisions the best we can, and those who start early and choose well will realize a better tomorrow than their misguided counterparts. Beg, borrow, or steel to get started because, as I have said on many pages, the early worm will be ahead of the herd.

Structure of Indecision

These are troubled times, and every day seems to be more disturbed than the next. Let us briefly look at the social dynamic that got us into this situation.

We've become a divided and exasperated society, bored by our riches, fed up with our inequality. We are frustrated with societal change caused by technological advancement, deceiving communication from corporate and governmental leaders, and a lack of substantive solutions in our neighborhoods. Almost no one felt like things were getting better, and then came COVID.

Humans: "Humans have a high propensity for proactive aggression."[17] Whether we are inherently so has been debated since we've had the leisure to do so. We are indeed a competitive species, and aggression is a tool of the competitive. Once we add scarcity to this mix, we transform away from those who would have us be pacifists in the face of diminishing resources —for example, clean air, fresh water, and dry land. When the chips are down, survival instincts will take over.

---

[17] Richard W. Wrangham, "Two Types of Aggression in Human Evolution," PNAS, 115, no. 2 (January 9, 2018), 245–258, https://doi.org/10.1073/pnas.1713611115.

Capitalism: A predictable maturation of this economic system results in a transition of opportunity and wealth from the underclasses to the elite. This pattern will continue without financial engineering, resulting in social unrest in the lower and middle echelons—read, violence in the streets.

Traditional U.S.A. Politics: Divergent ideologies have generally lobbied for their group's best interest, but in the end, the majority's interests prevailed. That is not so true today.

Politics Today: A polarized electorate makes "common good" decisions challenging to achieve and minority special interests disproportionately influential. Protect democracy.

Politicians Today: The best and brightest candidates quickly become disillusioned and withdraw from participation. What's left are the people we will need to depend upon going forward to help solve our most significant global challenges. They are generally *not the best and brightest*, have hardened special interests, and may have limited options after politics. We are screwed!

Democracy: Democracy is a doctrine of equality, majority rule, and fair representation. Unfortunately, this is not true today in a more acute way than in the past. Recent events have shown we are not all equal and election ethics have become distorted; now we are losing majority representation through gerrymandering and voting restrictions. You must exercise your right to vote if it is the last thing you do.

Summary: Thanks for staying with me through this mini civics review; it is essential to understand the core of why the battle to reverse global warming and to save the planet as we know it has already been lost. We have known about the need to cut carbon emissions, reduce the gallop toward higher and higher global temperatures, clean polluted waterways, increase carbon capture, and protect the planet for some time now. Despite the hard work of some very dedicated people, the collective effort has not been enough to get our economic, political, and governing systems to work together to thwart this now inevitable disaster. **We have run out of time.** It would be sheer folly to think that the people who led us into this debacle will want to, let alone be able to, lead us out.

We have to decipher individually how best to take care of our families going forward. These are discrete decisions and can only be decided by you, one at a time, and the time is now.

Unavoidable Inevitabilities

I've thrown around several dates and projections about timing to help your planning process, but there is a caveat. If we do nothing about reversing the rising temperatures, life for everyone will be most uncomfortable by 2050. Some will feel/are feeling life-changing impacts already. Therein lies the predictability conundrum. The imbalance created or precipitated by climate events will cause humans and maybe some of the one million species currently on the endangered list to transform their behavior. It is hard to tell precisely how that will play out. If we look at current events, the scarcity of traditional jobs over the last decade exposed a deep class divide in the United States. Changing political and climatic patterns have caused massive migrations toward Europe and North America that have not gone well.

It probably won't be an environmental calamity that does you or your children or your grandchildren in but rather one of the *unavoidable inevitabilities* that gets 'em before the weather: scarcity, wars, economic manipulation, civil unrest, animal uprising, ideological violence, planned or spontaneous pathogens, or just planetary exhaustion. While the climate as a catalyst for societal collapse, à la Jared Diamond[18], is not the only path forward, the pressure from environmental calamity will hasten societal dissonance, cutting the fragile thread holding our disparate international interests together. The point here is that it may be later than we think; this part, about the unpredictability of human action in the face of pending doom, is untested and challenging to foretell. So make sure the things on your "A List" are the most important; then get busy. Who knows; there may not even be time for grandchildren.

---

[18] Jared Diamond, Collapse (New York: Penguin Books, 2011).

Why Write This?

The reason to write *What to Do if Your Chute Doesn't Open!* is to challenge readers' awareness that action to stop global warming must accelerate now. It's probably naive of me to think that politicians and business leaders will come together and sacrifice today's gains for a cooler tomorrow, but that's exactly what we need them to do. They are not going to do this because it is the right thing but because they will make money and stay in power by so doing. The only way we can make this change happen is for all of us to maintain the pressure on these stewards of the future by using our purchasing power to support or refuse to support entities that are not aggressively working to curtail the imminent cooking of our home. Everyone needs to help!

Buy as little that contributes to warming as possible. This will be different for every one of us, but together this will add up. Every plastic straw you deny, the plastic bag you don't use at the grocery store, and the gas appliance you don't purchase will be noticed. Don't spend your money on things or in places where leadership is not actively developing and executing sustainable environmental practices. Plan your vacations, business meetings, and conventions in states[19] that are actively working on reducing carbon in the environment and pollutants in our neighborhoods while cooperating with other entities to make the coming boiling point less impactful. That's not always easy, but every action will help. I love to go to Florida to fish, but believe me, that is not going to happen anymore, and I'll miss it.

---

[19] "10 Greenest States in the U.S.," US News & World Report, April, 14, 2021.

Large and small business entities notice shifts in behavior and spending patterns. If they think they will not make as much money in the future because their state is ignoring science and contributing to global warming, they will get on board. While their initial engagement may be for the wrong reason, they will get that doing right by the planet is good business for us all.

I've never been much of a letter writer or politician visitor or online social influencer, but these are things we can all do at some level. Don't sit there and tell me you feel helpless. Get off your ass and write some letters, call a politician if you know one, send them this book. Write to companies whose products you buy or don't buy. Tell them they are doing a great job (Patagonia, Allbirds, Thredup) or a deplorable job (Chevron, Coca-Cola, PepsiCo, Nestlé, etc.); every action you take is essential. You can do something. You are not powerless—they just want you to think you are.

The planet's cooling is not up to THEM; it is up to US. If they were going to stop global warming, they would have done it by now, so leadership will not lead in a manner that will save this planet.

IT IS UP TO YOU!
Individually/together, this can be done.

Appendix

Rename Glacier National Park Contest
To enter, email your suggestion to igiveachute@gmail.com.
The top ten names will be forwarded to the National Park Service and the secretary of the Interior with a copy of this book.

Your Suggestion:_____
Your email:_____

Igiveachute Board
Become a member. The Committee will be responsible for determining Glacier renaming suggestions and which charities receive profit donations from What to Do if Your Chute Doesn't Open activities. Sign up today:

Name:_____
Email:_____

Fly Me to the Moon
To register:
Name: _____
Email: _____

Why I want to be part of the recolonization plan:
_____
_____

All book profits will be donated to the top Fly Me to the Moon charities, as determined by the 'Igiveachute' Committee in accordance with Charity Navigator qualifications and guidelines. Registration forms will be forwarded to Space X and Blue Origin, along with copies of the book.

Letters to Businesses and Elected Officials

These don't have to be complicated. Address your letter to a specific person, say what you feel, and give them a way to say thank you (email or address). The following paragraph will get you started, and you don't have to say any more than that. Remember, this is the power of the powerless; business and political types do pay attention to these letters if they get enough of them; they see them as potential dollars or votes.

Example:

Dear   ;
The purpose of this letter is to beg you to support efforts to end global warming and the daily pollution of our planet. We are dependent upon you to exercise sound judgment to preserve the incredible natural resources we have inherited from our forefathers so that we might pass them on unspoiled to the generations of the future.

Sincerely,

Your Name
I Give a Chute about Global Cooling

About the Author

I was born in the Eastern United States and transitioned to the West for graduate school. I owned a leather shop, did time as a janitor, college lecturer, poet, road hippie, artist, poverty program researcher, salesman, business entrepreneur, CEO (NYSE), and writer. I know, it sounds like I need professional help, and maybe you're right.

I've been more than a little frustrated in the way the environmental movement has gone. Of course, there are great folks out there working hard and making progress in many important areas. They just haven't been able to make the kind of headway we need to get local, state, and world leaders to make the kinds of commitments necessary to take back control of our planet. So it is my hope that by writing this snarky little book, I might reach some of those that have not yet been listening/acting. We desperately need your help to reach out and let decision-makers of all types know that NOW is the time to make their move to **Stop Global Warming** and be on the right side of history before there is history no more. I appreciate your being a part of this endeavor.